selected by James Rae

repertoire explorer flute 1

Graded pieces for beginners

Abwechslungsreiche Spielstücke für Anfänger

Piano part

Preface

Teachers seeking further material to enlarge their pupil's repertoire but without having to search through quantities of music that is technically too challenging for their pupil's level, need look no further.

This selection of pieces from classical to modern and studies of all kinds, is suitable for each of grades 1, 2 and 3. I have kept in mind the technical requirements for major music examinations at each level.

Whether examinations are undertaken or not, this collection presents an opportunity for any pupil in their early years of tuition to broaden their musical experiences and explore the wide variety of music that is within their grasp.

James Rae

Vorwort

Lehrerinnen und Lehrer müssen auf der Suche nach Material, um das Repertoire ihrer Schülerinnen und Schülern zu erweitern, nun nicht mehr Unmengen von Notenheften durchstöbern, um fündig zu werden.

Diese Auswahl von klassischen bis modernen Stücken und Etüden ist geeignet für Anfänger bis leicht fortgeschrittene Spielerinnen und Spieler. Sie fand unter Berücksichtigung der Schwierigkeitsgrade des englischen Musikprüfungssystems statt.

Unabhängig davon, ob die Ausbildung nun diesem Prüfungssystem folgt oder nicht, bietet die Sammlung allen Lernenden in den ersten Jahren die Gelegenheit, den Fähigkeiten entsprechend ihre musikalischen Erfahrungen zu erweitern und eine große Vielfalt an Musikstücken zu erkunden.

James Rae

Préface

Vous êtes enseignant et souhaitez élargir le répertoire de vos élèves sans recourir à des morceaux d'un niveau technique trop élevé ? Ne cherchez plus !

La présente sélection de pièces et études de toutes sortes, classiques et modernes, convient aux niveaux 1, 2 et 3. En faisant mon choix, j'ai aussi tenu compte des exigences techniques des examens musicaux significatifs de chaque niveau.

Que l'on choisisse ou non de gravir les échelons du système d'examens, cette sélection est pour l'élève en début d'apprentissage une occasion d'élargir le champ de son expérience musicale et d'explorer la grande variété des œuvres à sa portée.

James Rae

Contents

Inhalt

Tables des matières

The Skye Boat Song

Traditional
arr. James Rae

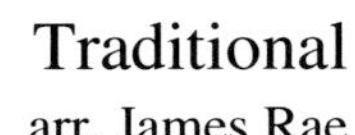

21
mf
mf
26
p
8
p
31
rit.
dal 𝄋 al Coda
8
loco
Coda
37
rit.
8 optional

Grade 1

March from "Rinaldo"

George Frideric Handel
(1685–1759)
ed. Gerhard Braun and Siegfried Petrenz

Allegro

12

16

20
1.
2.

Grade 1

Original Dances, No. 5

Franz Schubert
(1797–1828)

Universal Edition UE 21 457

Grade 1

Morning has Broken

Traditional
arr. John Reeman

Universal Edition UE 21 457

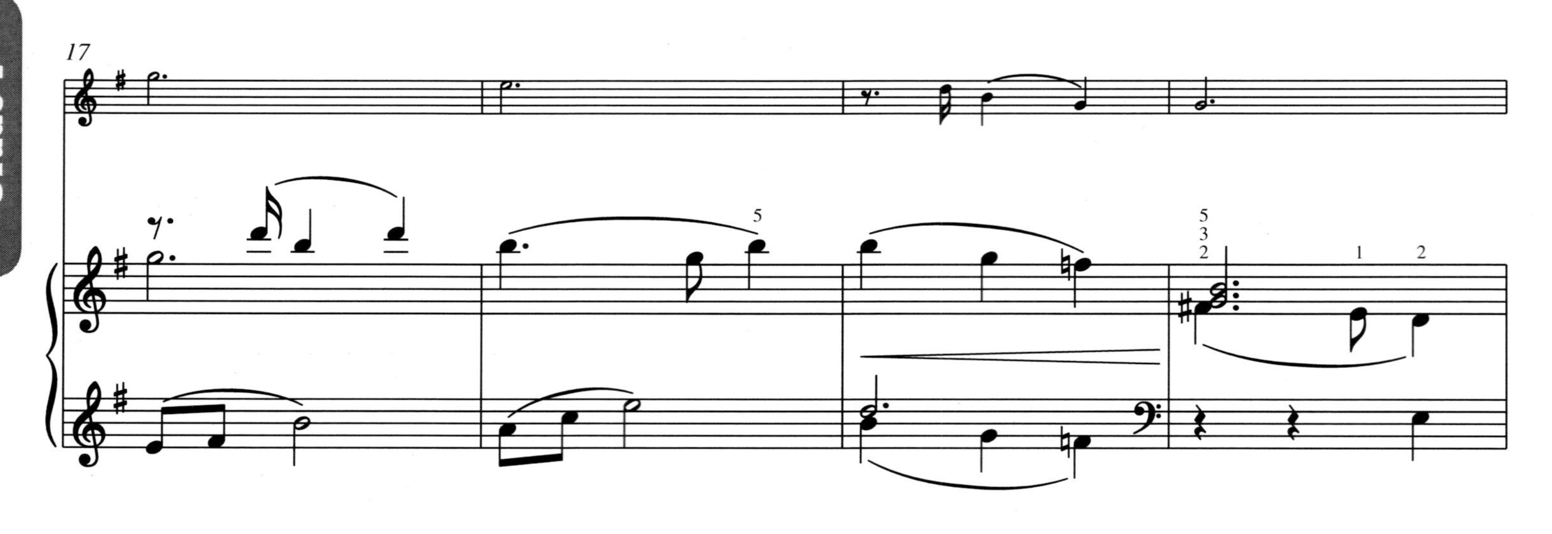

rall.
cresc.
cresc.

a tempo
f
f

Grade 1

Out and About

James Rae
(*1957)

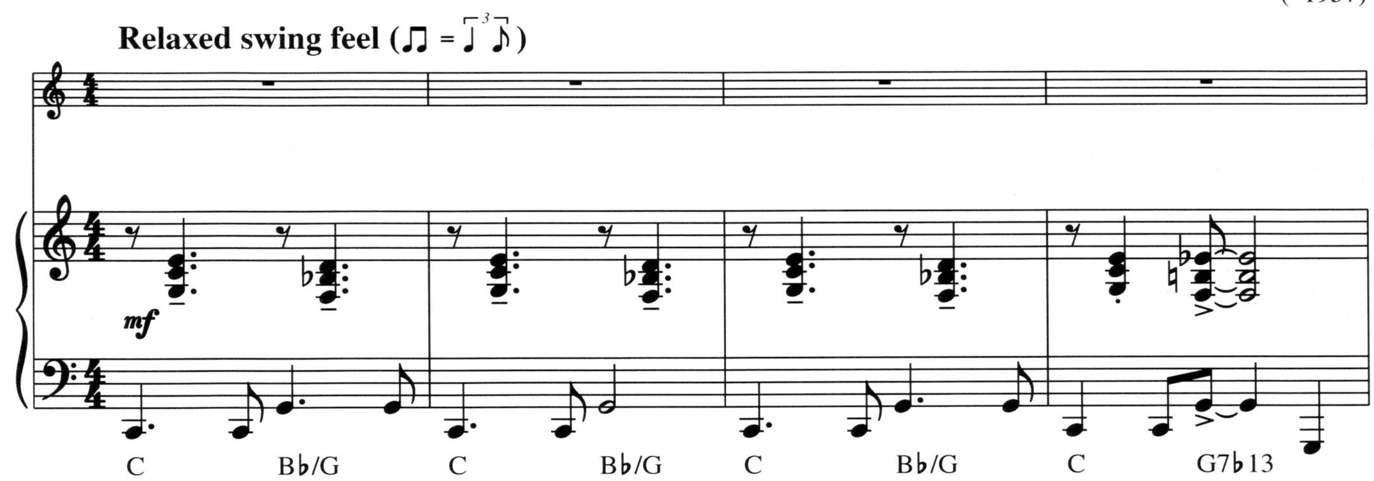

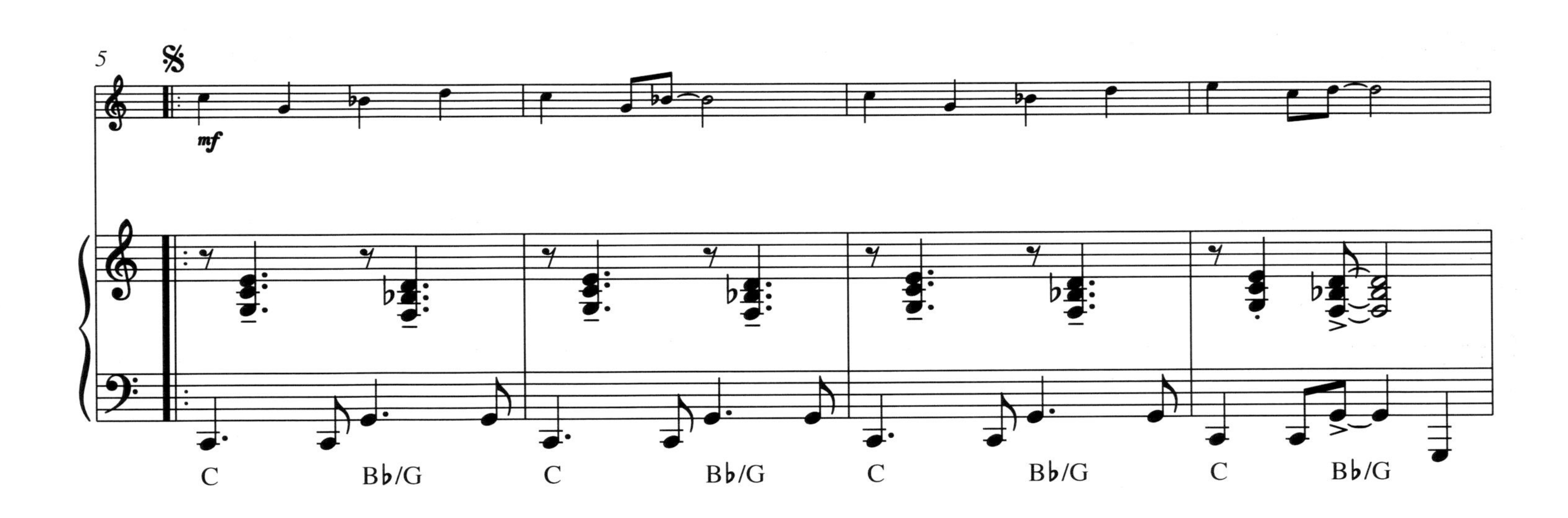

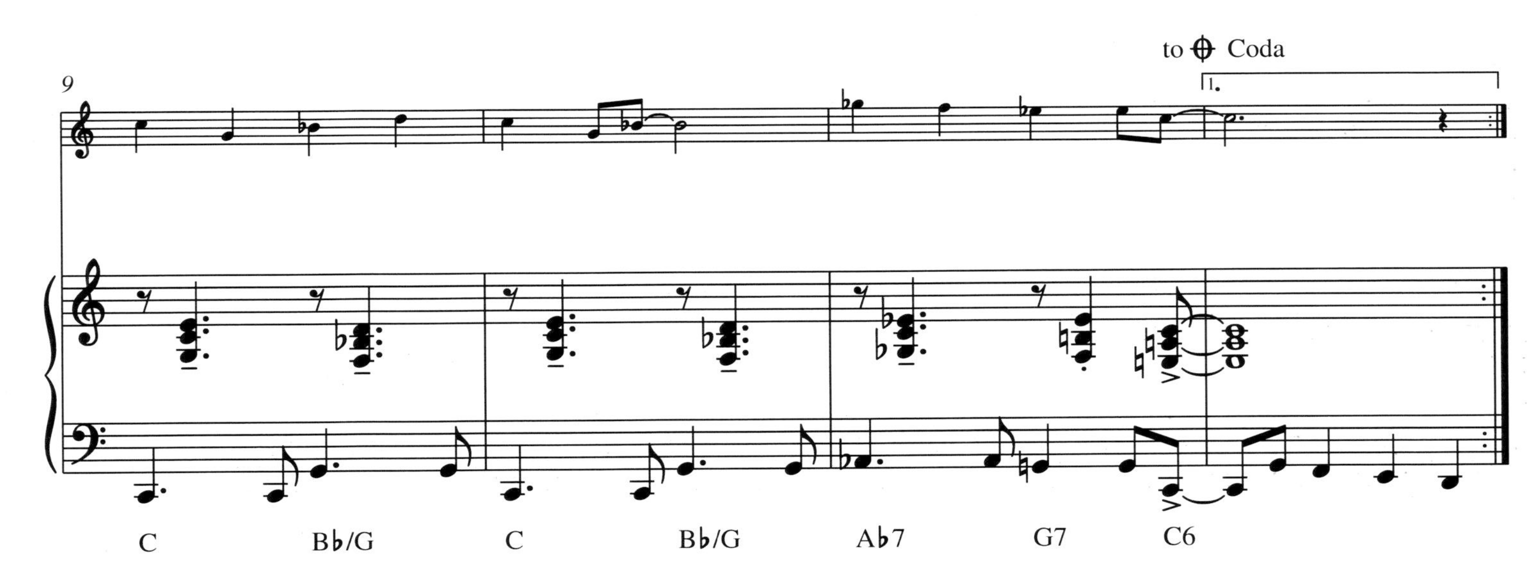

13
2.
f
Fmaj7
Cmaj7/9

16
Fmaj7
Cmaj7/9
Fmaj7
Cmaj7/9
Am7

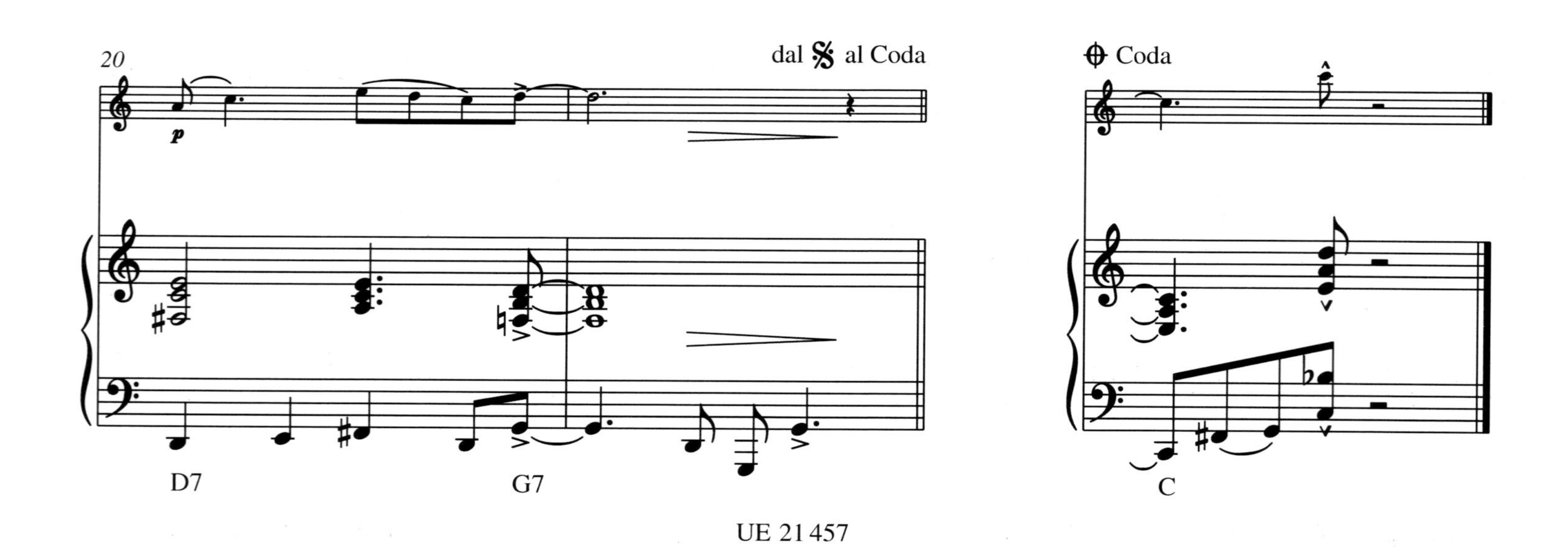
20
dal 𝄋 al Coda
p
D7
G7
Coda
C

Rum Point

James Rae
(*1957)

Solid 'reggae' feel ♩ = 96

Universal Edition UE 21 457

Grade 1

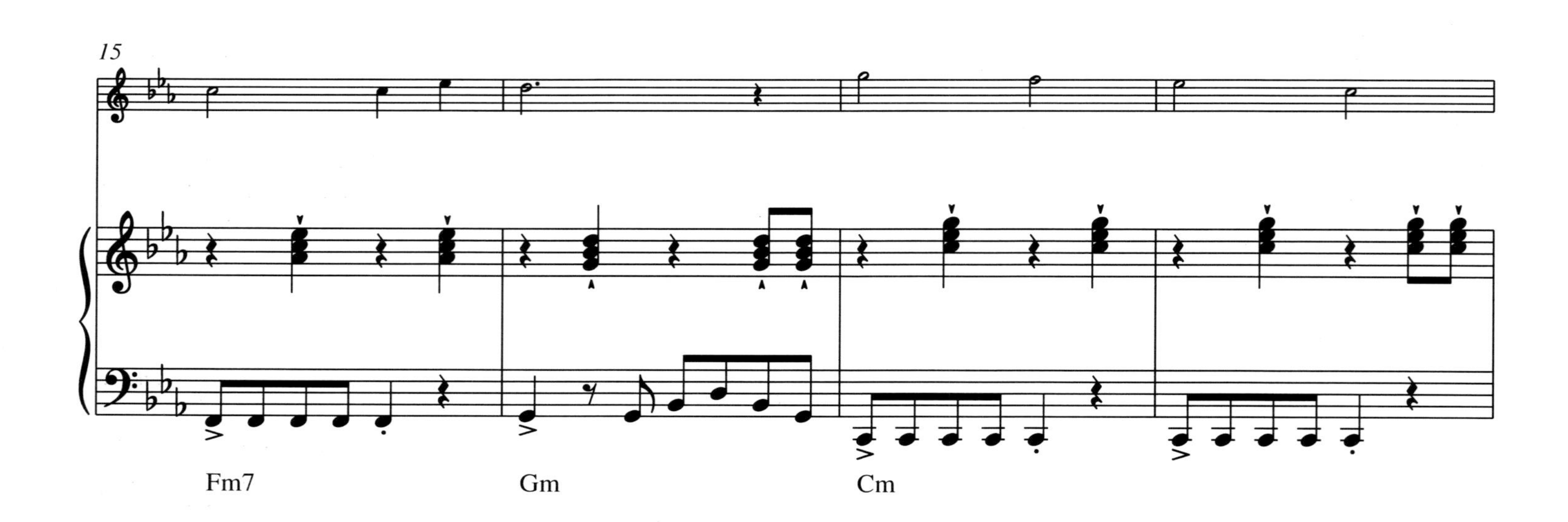

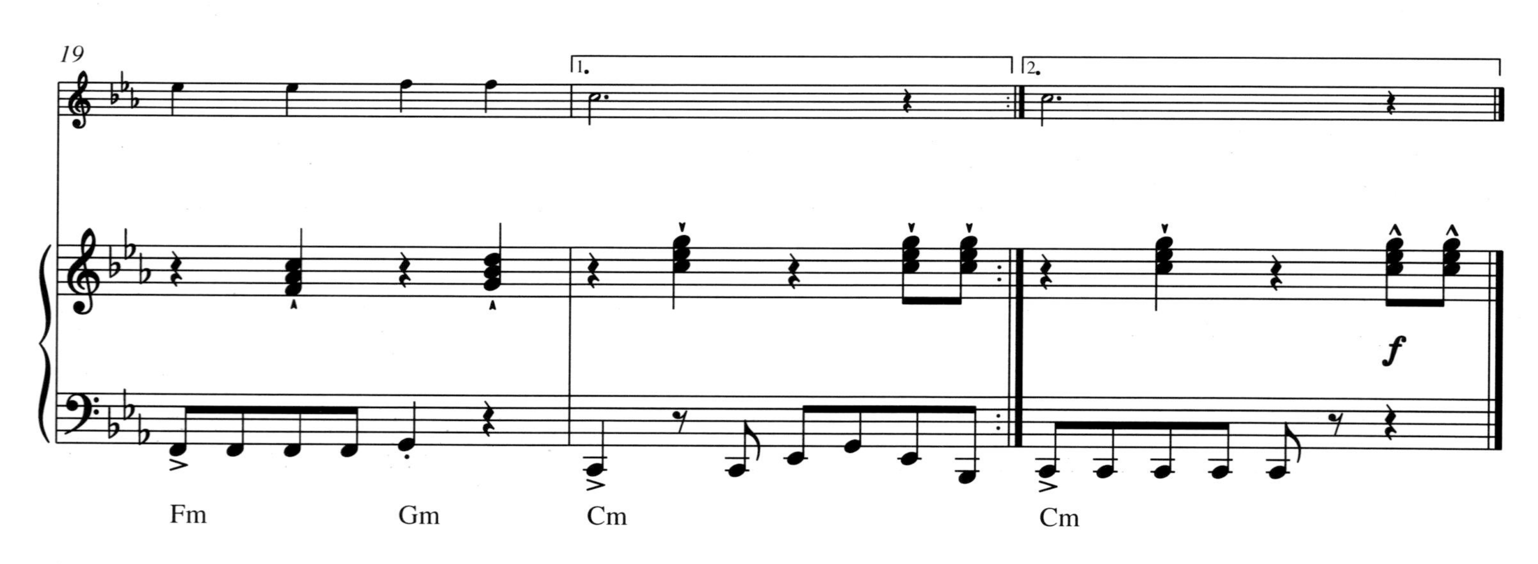

Grade 1

Counting Rhyme

Helmut Bornefeld
(1906–1990)

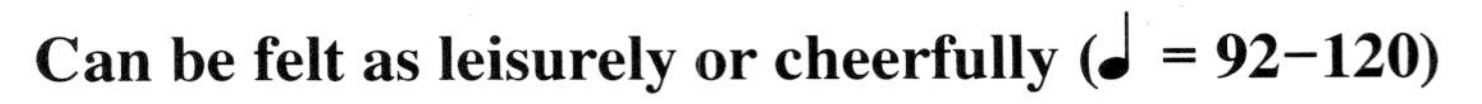

Ecossaise

Ludwig van Beethoven
(1770–1827)
arr. Peter Kolman

Grade 2

Allegro giusto

Grade 2

Lord of the Dance

Traditional
arr. John Reeman

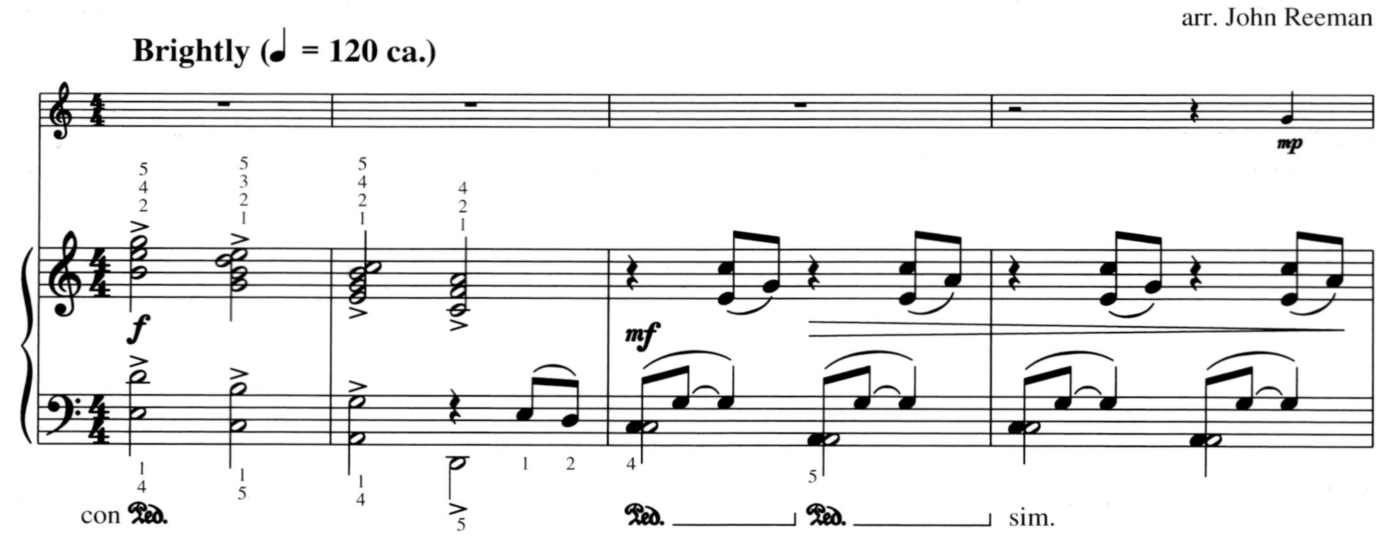

Grade 2

rall.

March in C Major

Louis de Caix d'Hervelois
(1670–1760)
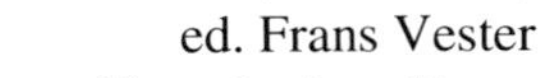
ed. Frans Vester
figured bass by Jane Eston

Grade 2

Grade 2

Suite Paysanne Hongroise

6.

Béla Bartók
(1881–1945)
arr. Paul Arma

7.

Poco più vivo (♩ = 136) (quasi trio)
f
f
5
mf
mf
f
f
Allegretto
9
p leggiero
sfz
p
14
dim. e calando
pp
dim. e calando
pp

Grade 2

Summer Evening

John Reeman
(*1946)

Grade 2

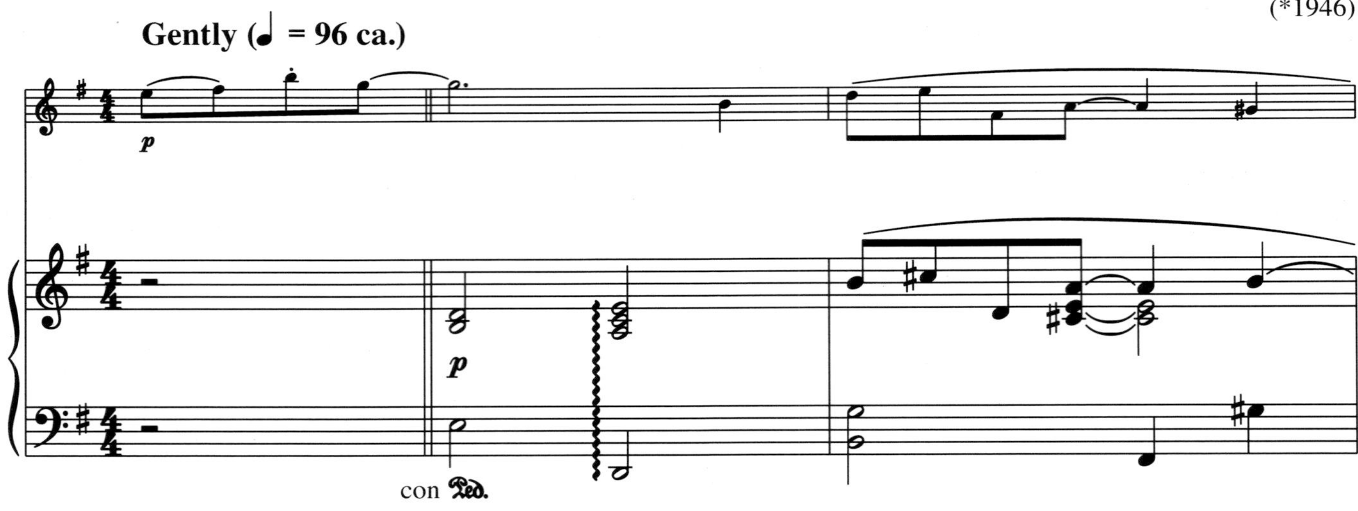

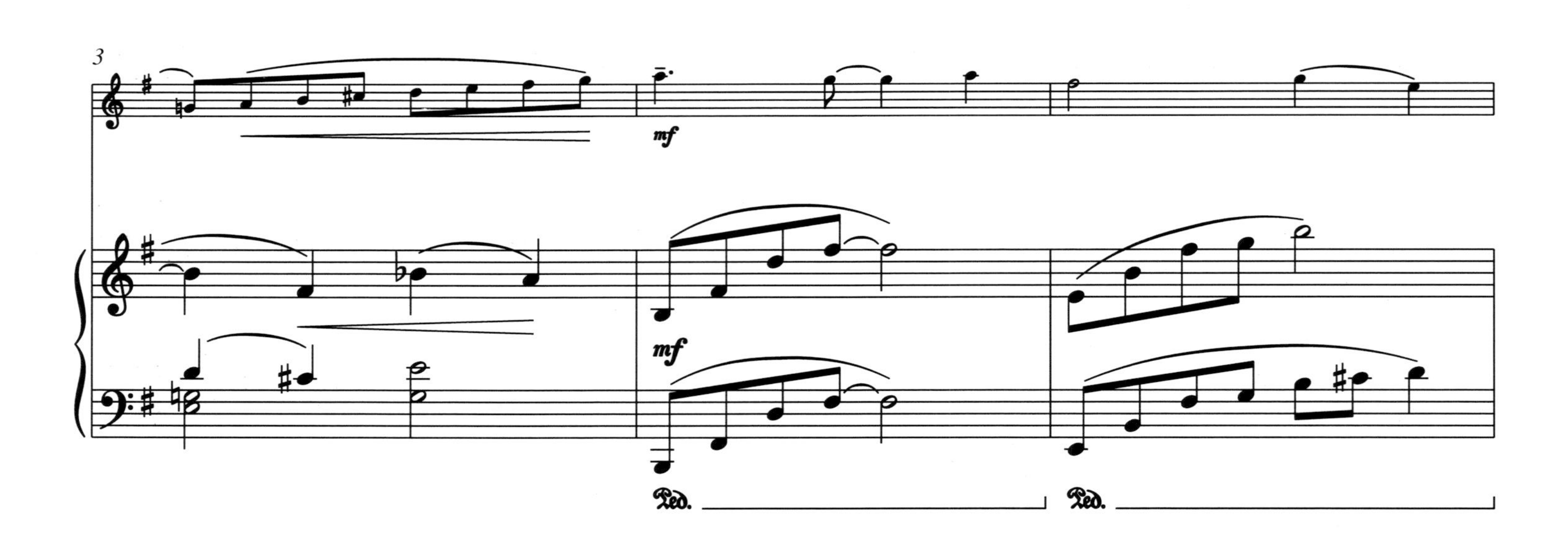

Universal Edition UE 21 457

9
p
mf
f
p
mf
f
Ped.
Ped.
Ped.

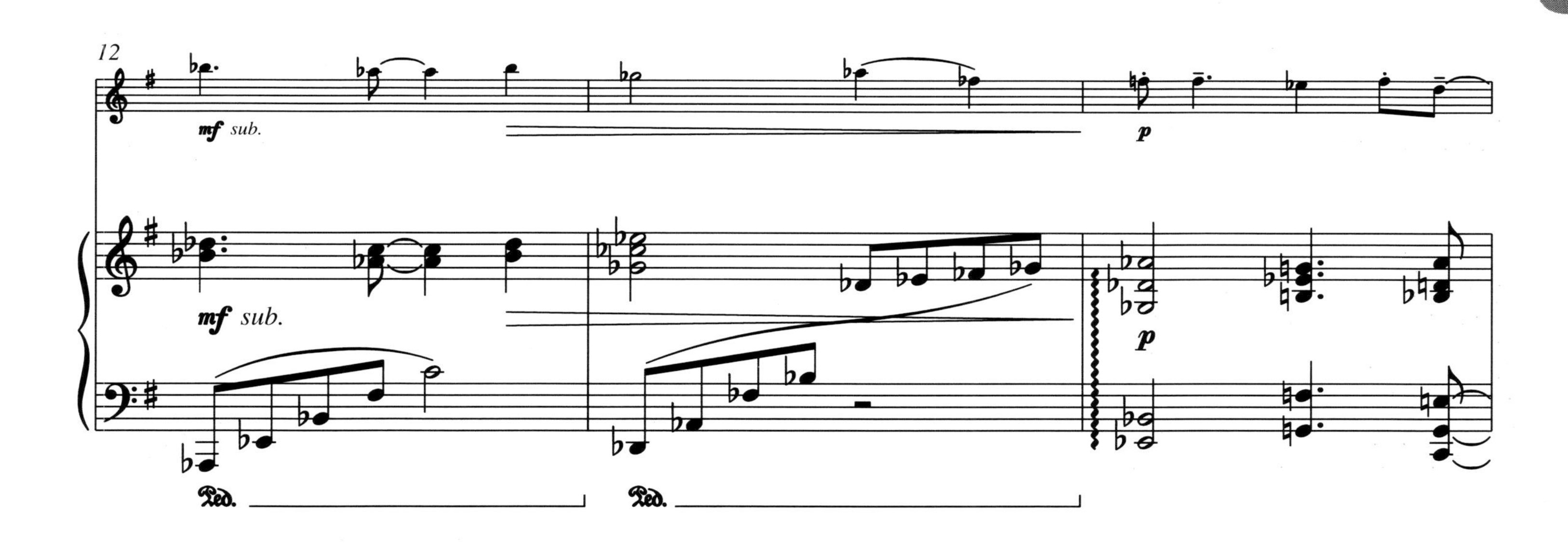
12
mf sub.
p
mf sub.
p
Ped.
Ped.

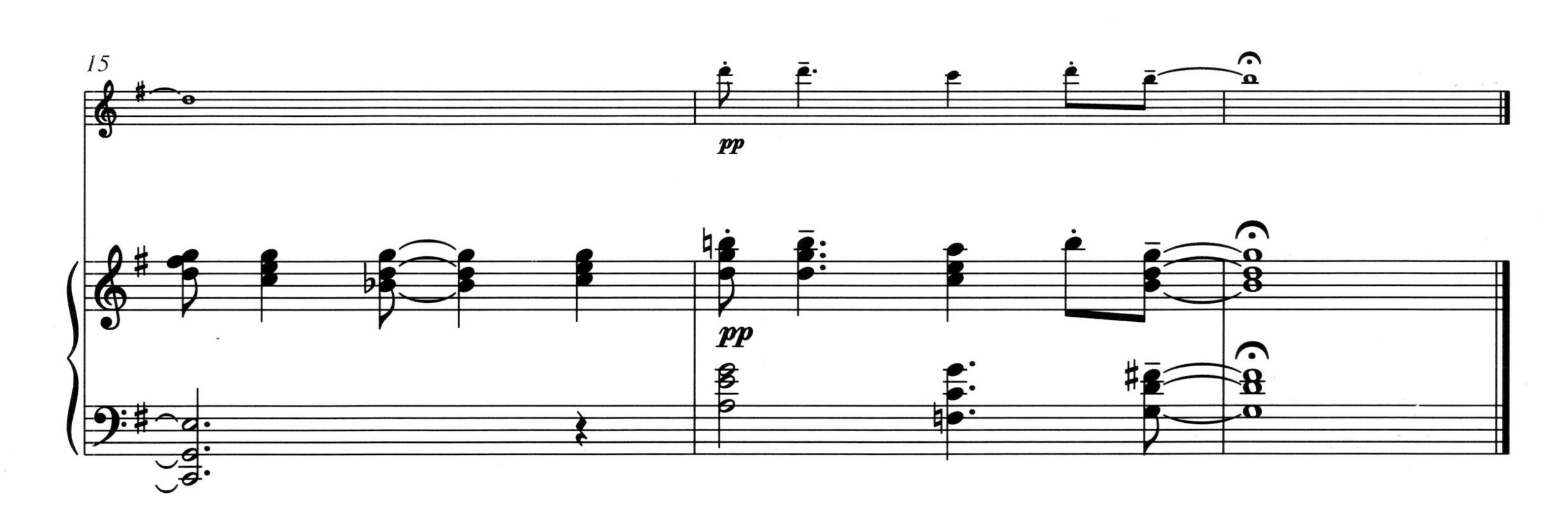
15
pp
pp

Hacienda

James Rae
(*1957)

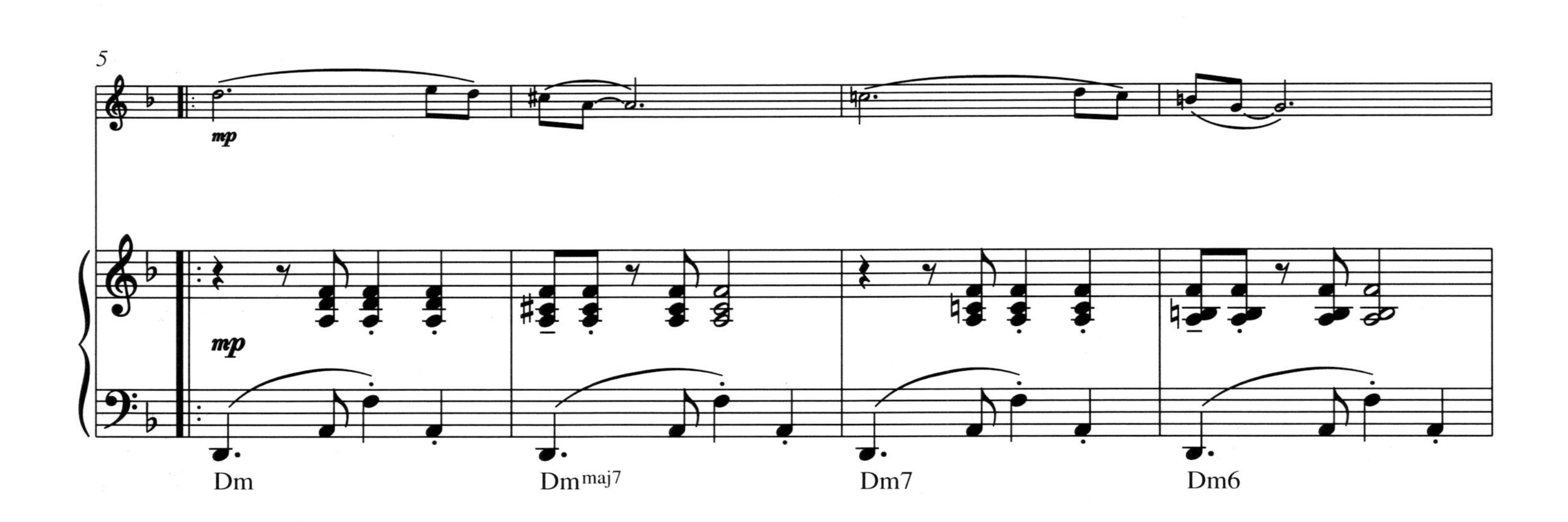

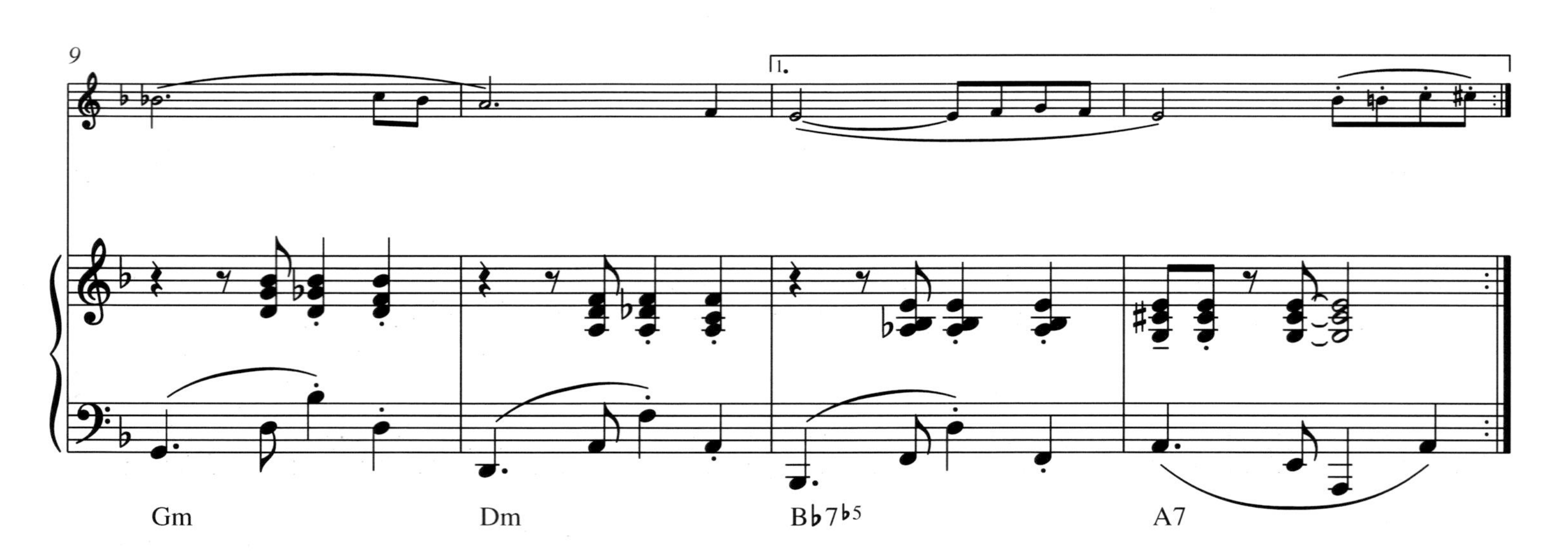

Universal Edition UE 21 457

13
2.
mf
B♭7♭5
A7
Dm
C9
F
C9
18
F
A7
Dm
B♭7♭5
22
ad lib.
8
f
A7
Dm
Dmmaj7
Dm7
26
p
Dm6
Gm
Dm
B♭7♭5
A7
Dm
Dm9add6
Grade 2

Papageno's Aria from "The Magic Flute"

Wolfgang Amadeus Mozart
(1756–1791)
arr. Peter Kolman

Grade 3

Grade 3

Polonaise in D Major

Georg Philipp Telemann
(1681–1767)
ed. Frans Vester
figured bass by Jane Eston

Grade 3

Universal Edition UE 21 457

11

14

17

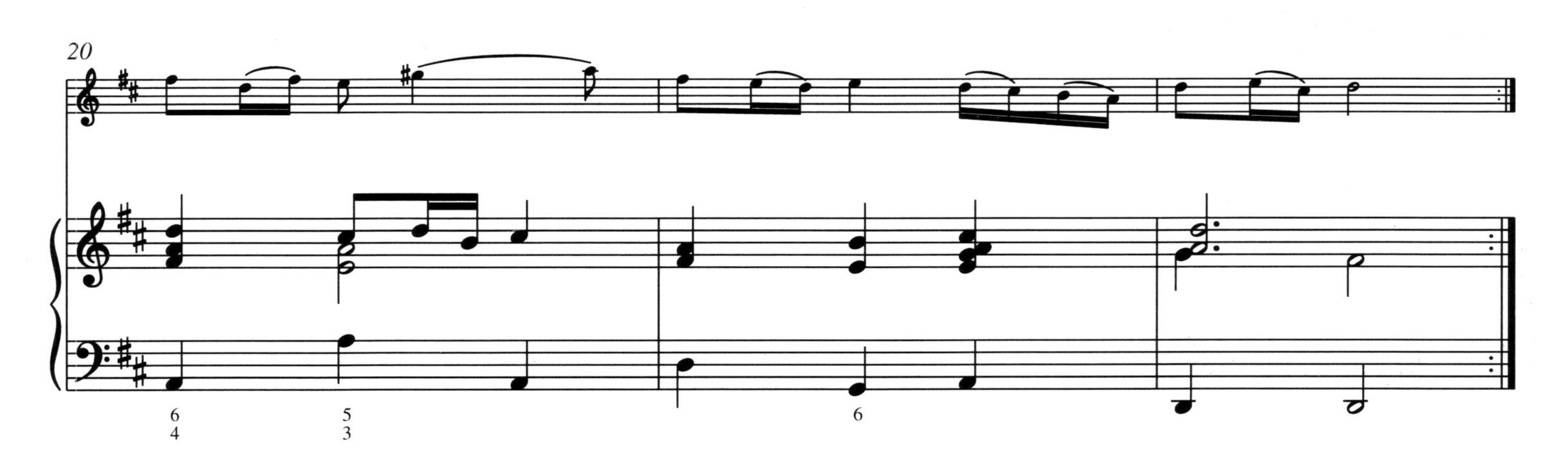
20

Old French Song

Pyotr Ilyich Tchaikovsky
(1840–1893)

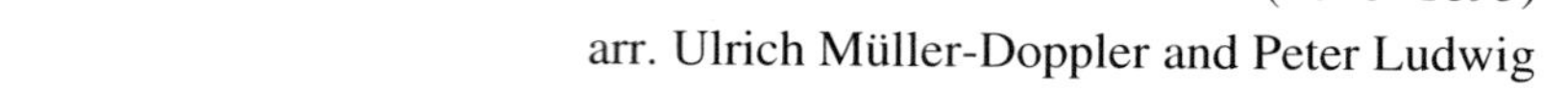
arr. Ulrich Müller-Doppler and Peter Ludwig

Very moderate

rit.
Grade 3

Cha Cha Calypso

James Rae
(*1957)

Relaxed 'cha cha cha' feel

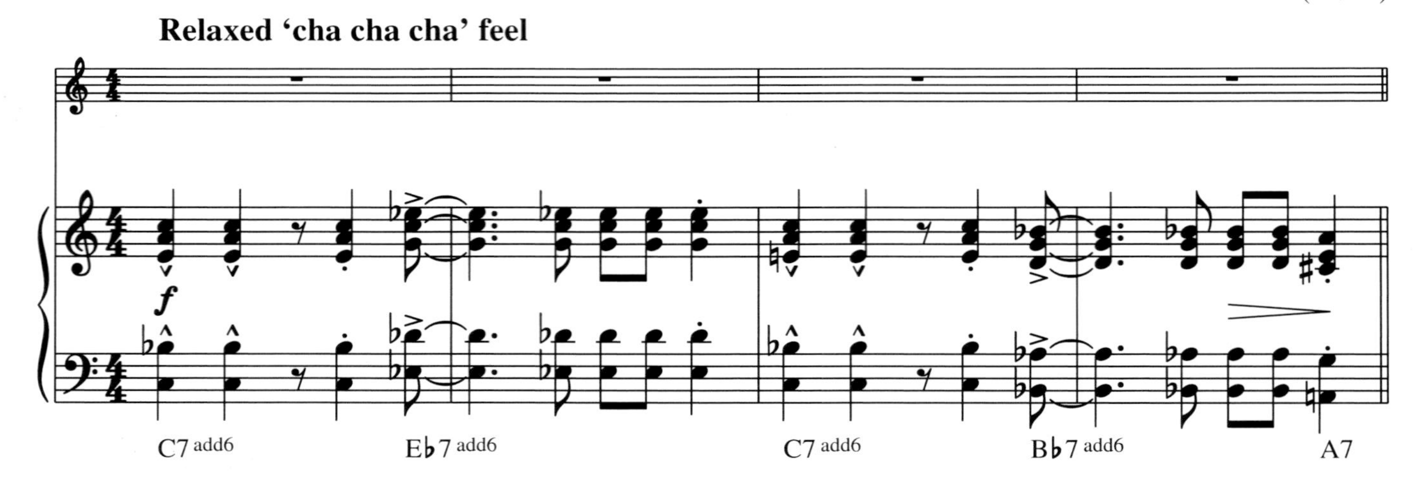

Grade 3

13
f
mf
C6/9
C7 add6
No Chord
Gm7
C7
Gm7
C7♭9
sim.
F maj7
18
cresc.
f
Am7
D7
Am7
D7
G7
G7 add6
B♭7 add6
22
gliss.
mf
G7 add6
F7 add6
G7 add6
Dm7
G7
Dm7
G9
B♭m/G
C maj7
26
f
A9
A7♭9
Dm7
G7
Dm7
G7
C6/9
C7 add6
No Chord

Grade 3

The Londonderry Air

Traditional
arr. James Rae

repertoire explorer flute 1

Graded pieces for beginners

Abwechslungsreiche Spielstücke für Anfänger

Flute part

Flute

Contents

Inhalt

Tables des matières

Grade 1

Grade 2

Grade 3

Grade 1

Fotokopieren
gesetzlich
verboten
Photocopying prohibited by law

The Skye Boat Song

Traditional
arr. James Rae
Gently rocking
4
p dolce
9
p
15
to Coda
21
mf
26
p
31
rit.
36
dal 𝄋 al Coda
Coda
rit.
8 optional

March from "Rinaldo"

George Frideric Handel
(1685–1759)
ed. Gerhard Braun and Siegfried Petrenz
Allegro
4
8
tr
1.
2.

Original Dances, No. 5

Franz Schubert
(1797–1828)

Morning has Broken

Traditional
arr. John Reeman

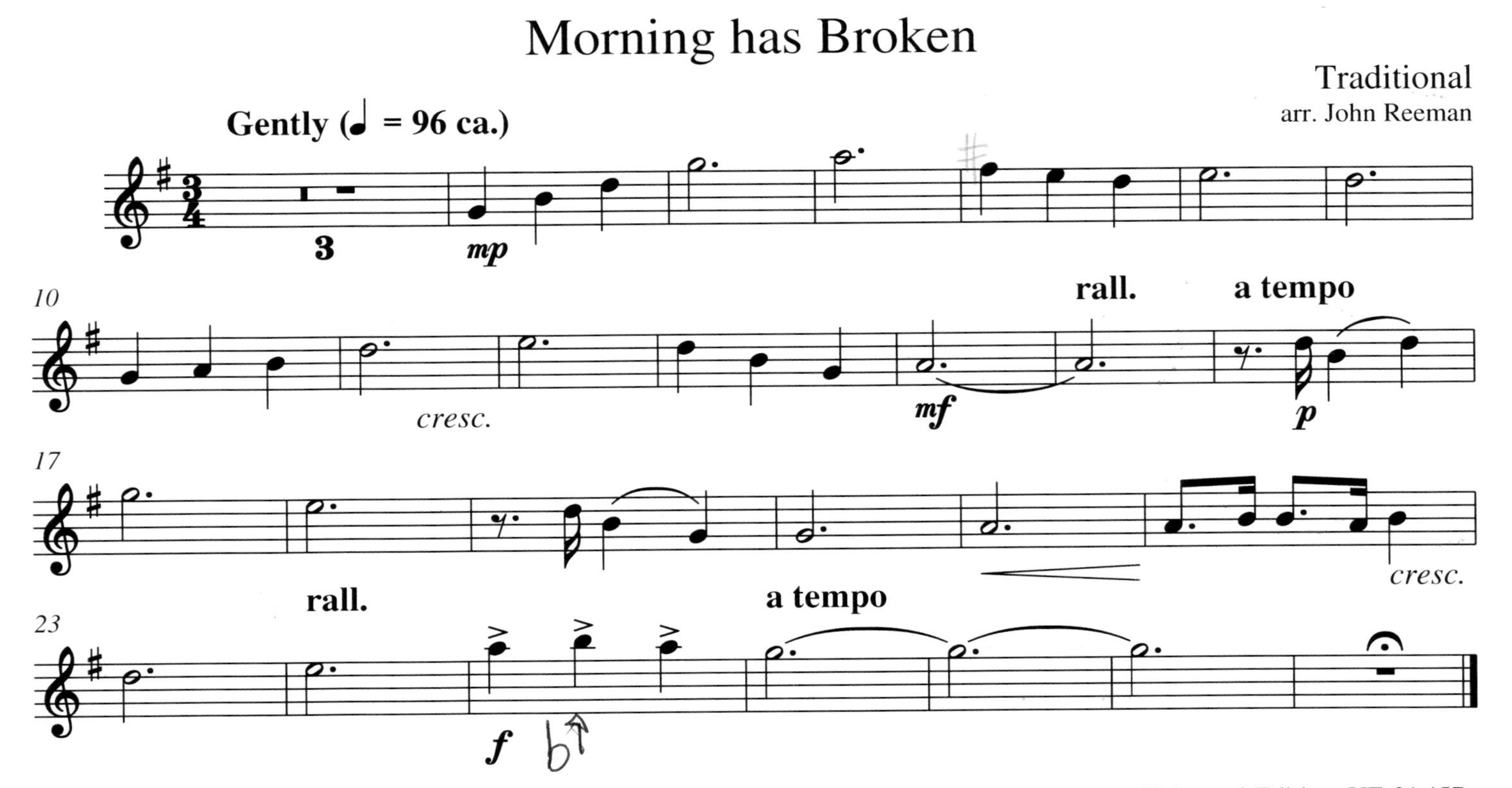

Out and About

James Rae
(*1957)

Relaxed swing feel

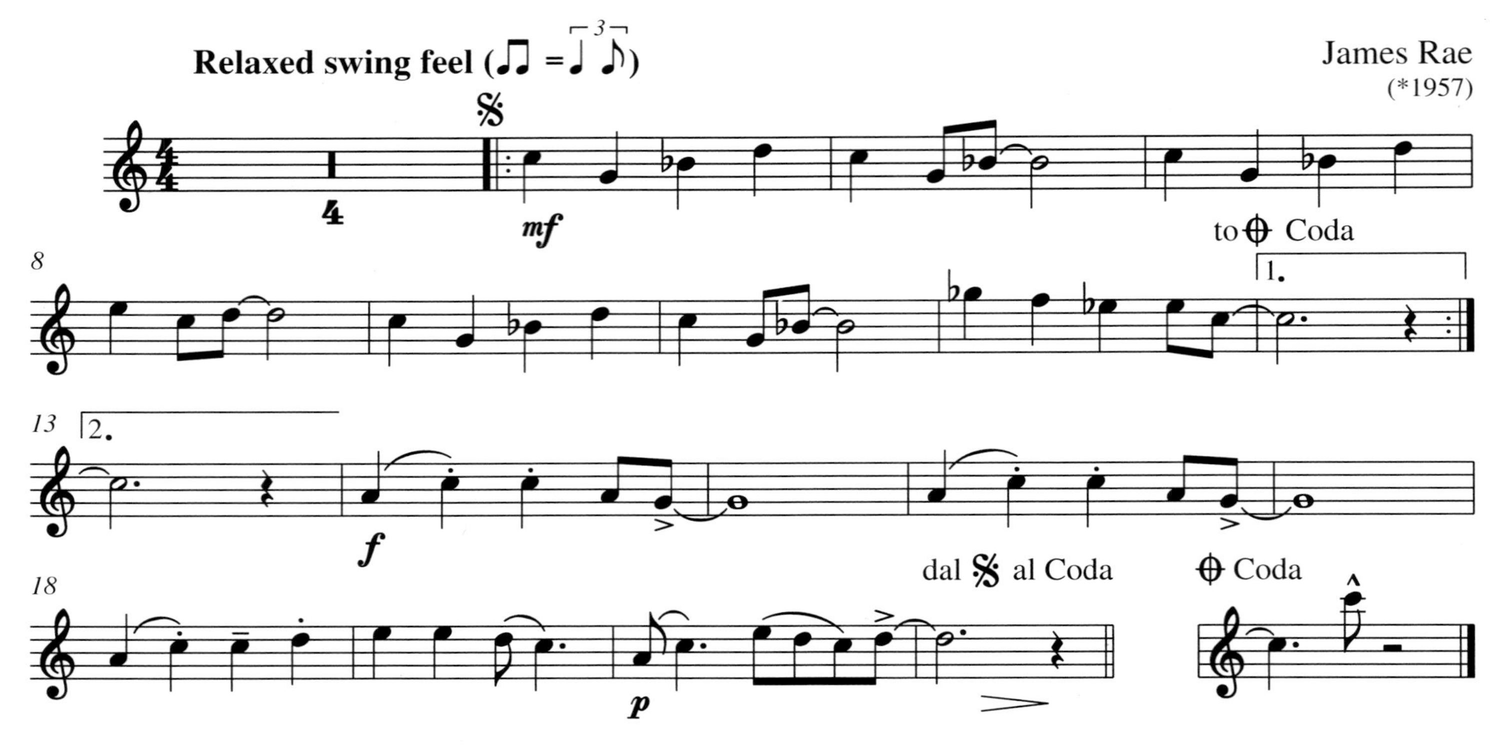

Rum Point

James Rae
(*1957)

Solid 'reggae' feel ♩ = 96

Counting Rhyme

Helmut Bornefeld
(1906–1990)

Can be felt as leisurely or cheerfully (♩ = 92–120)

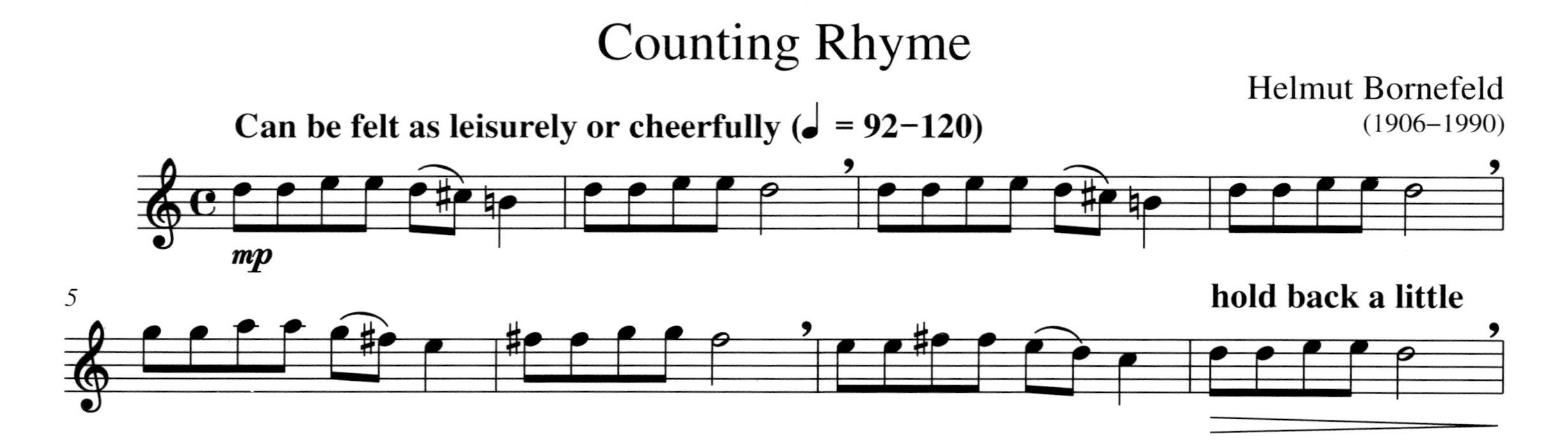

9
first tempo
mp
13
only slightly broader
Allegretto
Ernesto Köhler
(1849–1907)
ed. Frans Vester
Allegretto
mp
6
11

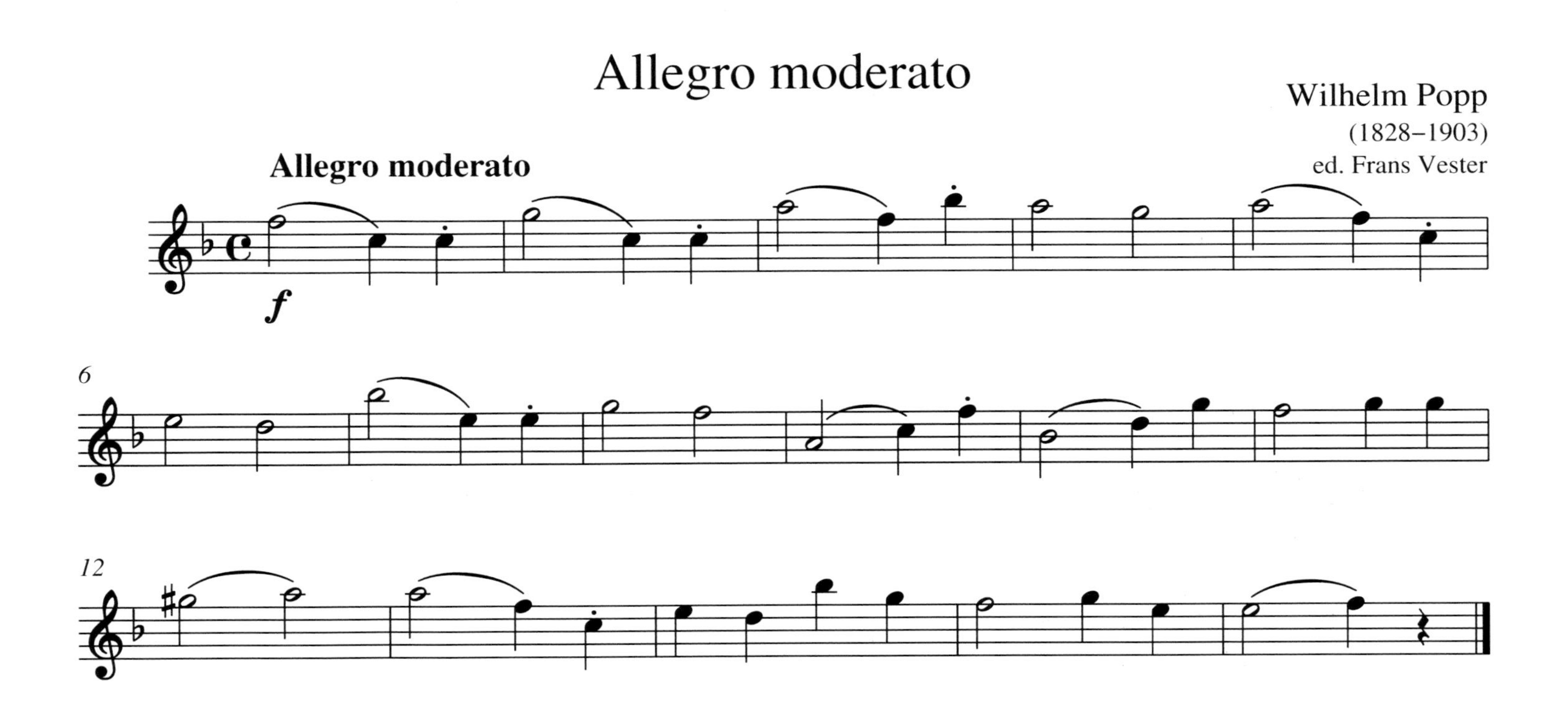
Allegro moderato
Wilhelm Popp
(1828–1903)
ed. Frans Vester
Allegro moderato
f
6
12

Les a Dieu de Bagnolet, Minuet 1

Nicolas Chédville
(1705–1782)
ed. Hannah König

In the Wings

James Rae
(*1957)

Autumn Clouds

James Rae
(*1957)

That'll do Nicely!

James Rae
(*1957)

The Time has Come

James Rae
(*1957)

Ecossaise

Ludwig van Beethoven
(1770–1827)
arr. Peter Kolman

Grade 2

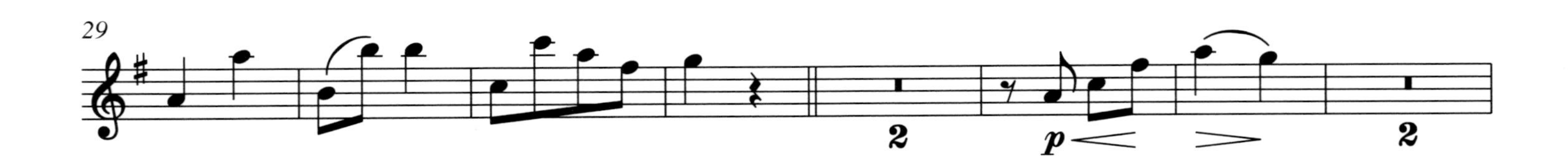

Lord of the Dance

Traditional
arr. John Reeman

Brightly (♩ = 120 ca.)

Grade 2

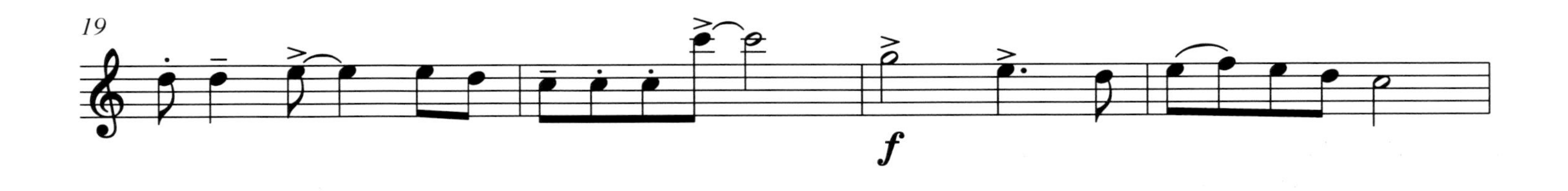

March in C Major

Louis de Caix d'Hervelois
(1670–1760)
ed. Frans Vester

Suite Paysanne Hongroise

Béla Bartók
(1881–1945)
arr. Paul Arma

6.

Universal Edition UE 21 457a

Grade 2

Summer Evening

John Reeman
(*1946)

Hacienda

James Rae
(*1957)

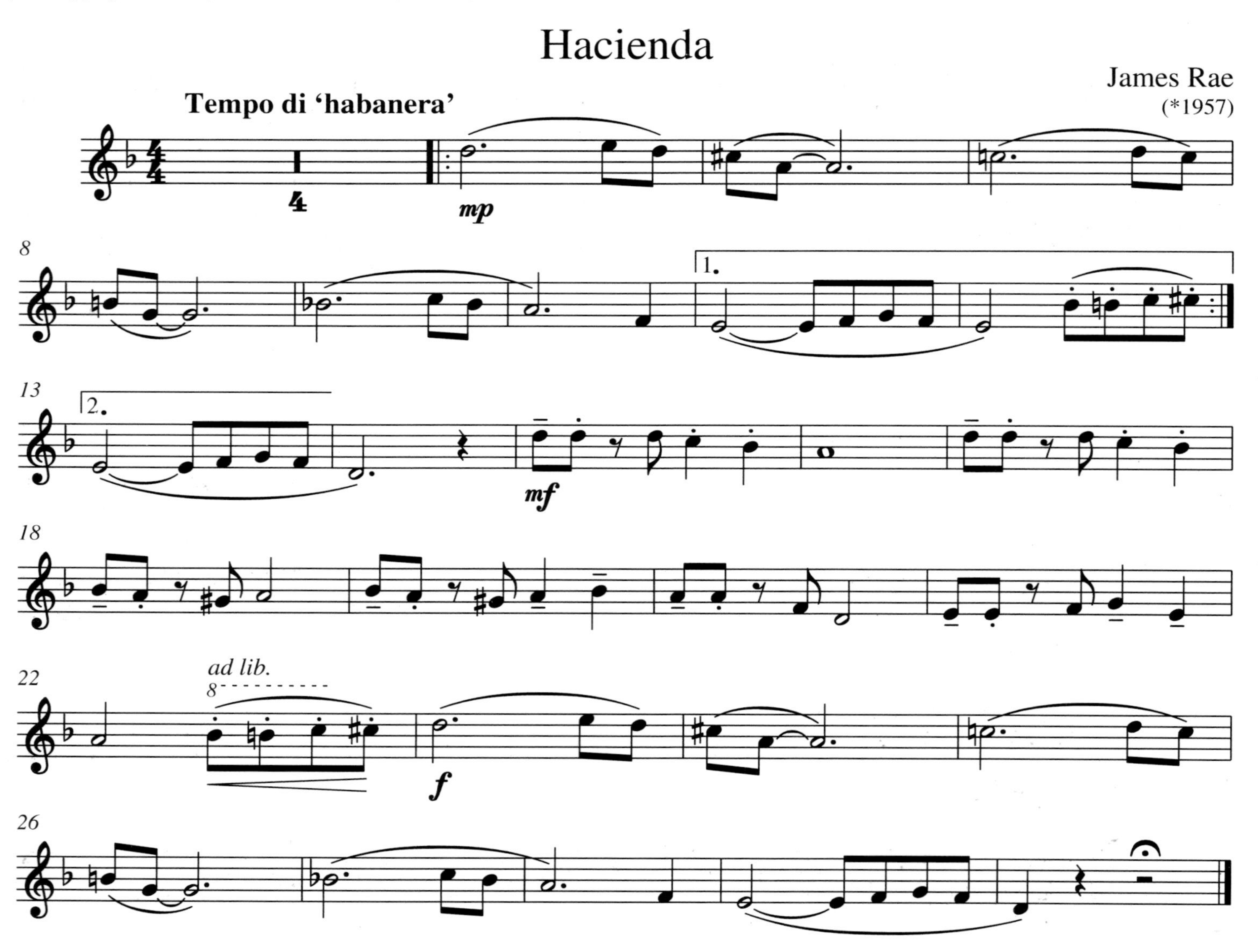

Two Minuets in D Major

George Frideric Handel
(1685–1759)
ed. Martin Heidecker and Siegfried Petrenz

HWV 505

9

tr

16

HWV 556

Minuet from "Don Giovanni"

Wolfgang Amadeus Mozart
(1756–1791)
arr. Karl Heinz Füssl

Andante

mf – p

6

mp

11

cresc.

mf

Open Spaces

James Rae
(*1957)

Grade 2

Limbo!

James Rae
(*1957)

Mixin' It!

James Rae
(*1957)

Maestoso

Giuseppe Gariboldi
(1833–1905)
ed. Frans Vester

Papageno's Aria from "The Magic Flute"

Wolfgang Amadeus Mozart
(1756–1791)
arr. Peter Kolman

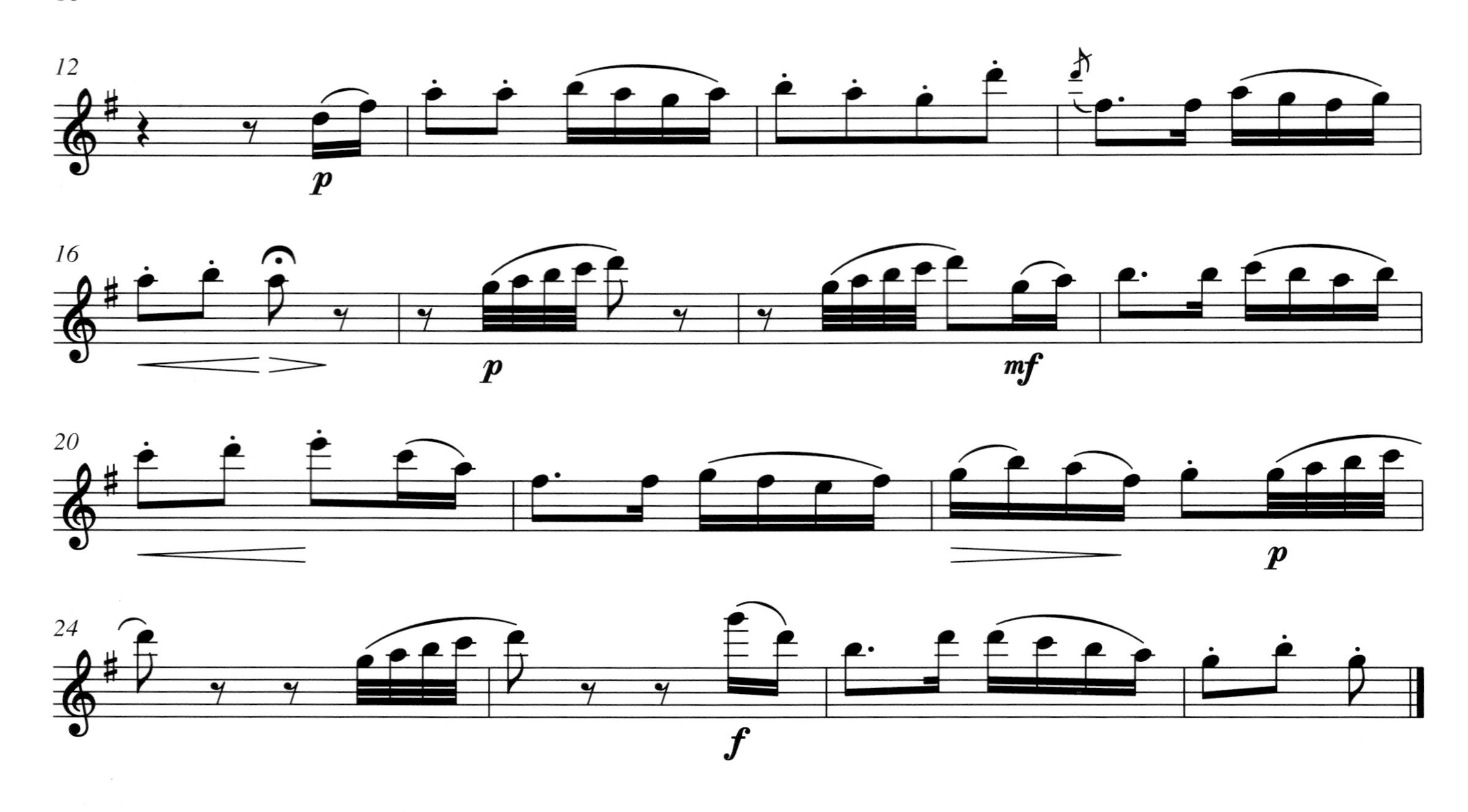

Polonaise in D Major

Georg Philipp Telemann
(1681–1767)
ed. Frans Vester

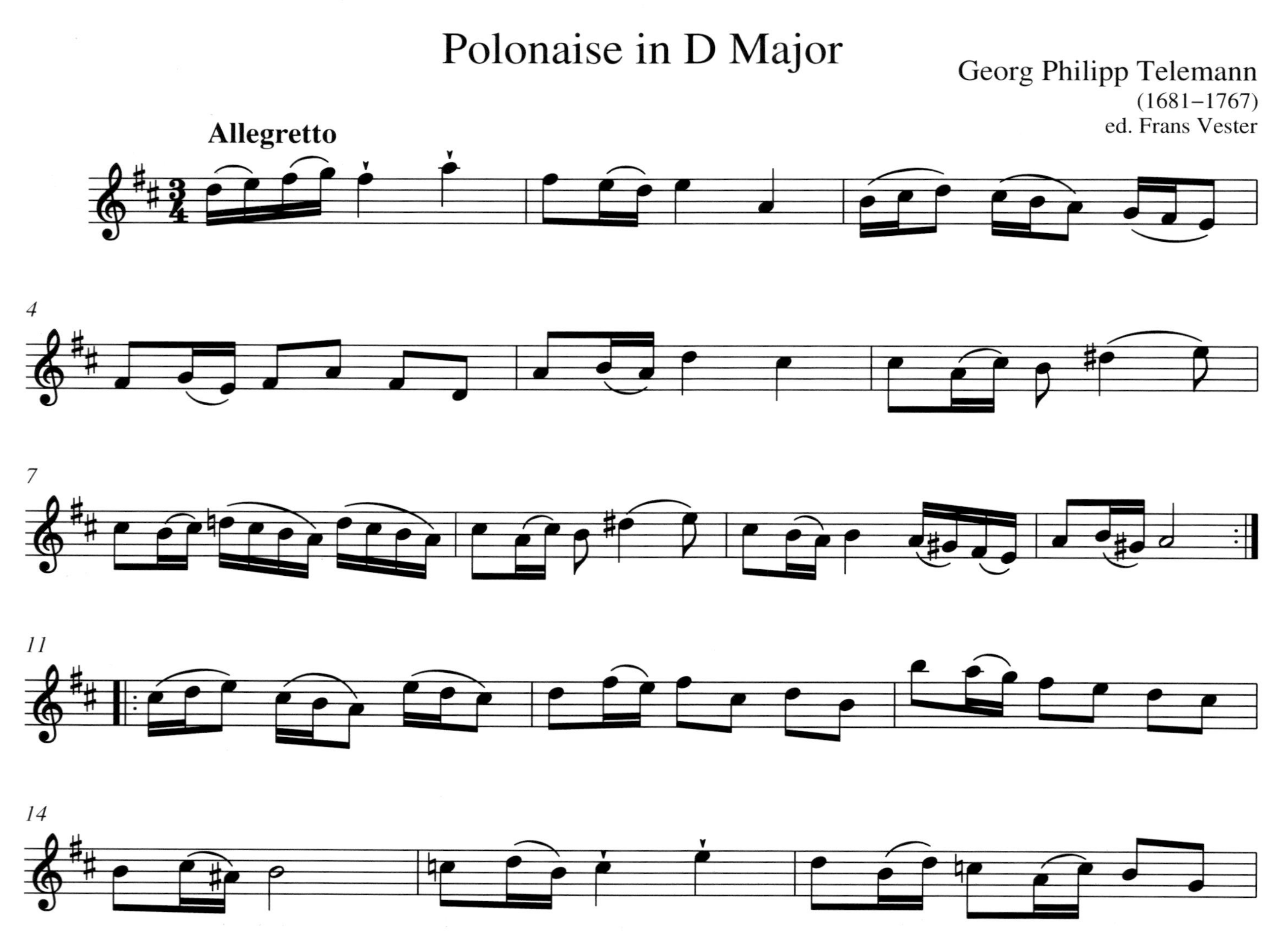

Old French Song

Pyotr Ilyich Tchaikovsky
(1840–1893)
arr. Ulrich Müller-Doppler and Peter Ludwig

Cha Cha Calypso

James Rae
(*1957)

Grade 3

The Londonderry Air

Traditional
arr. James Rae

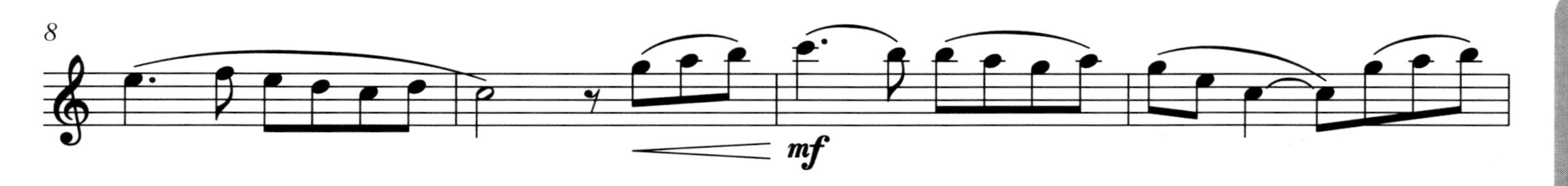

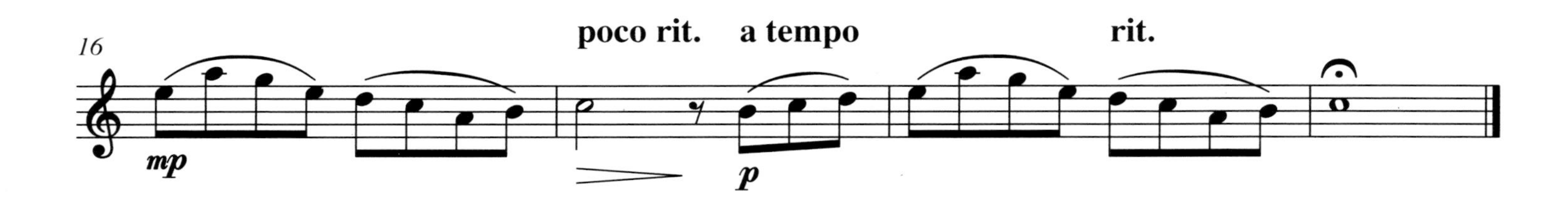

Universal Edition UE 21 457a

Allegro moderato

Ernesto Köhler
(1849–1907)
ed. Frans Vester

Grade 3

Allegretto

Heinrich Soussmann
(1796–1848)
ed. Frans Vester

The Irish Washerwoman

Traditional
arr. James Rae

Estländler

Arvo Pärt
(*1935)

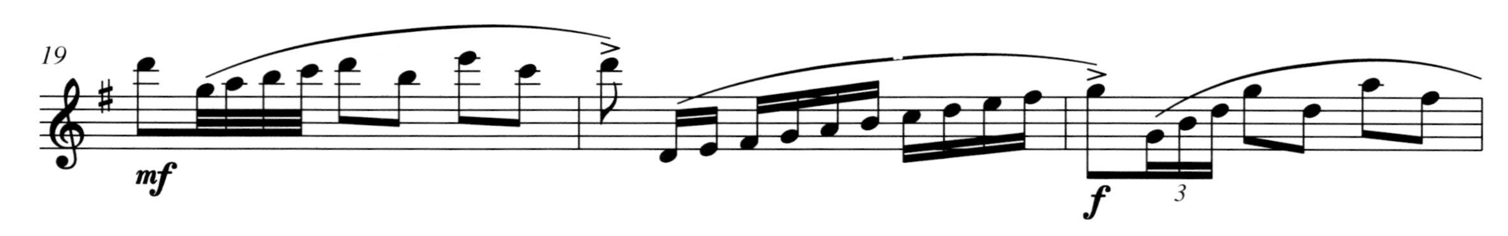

Grade 3

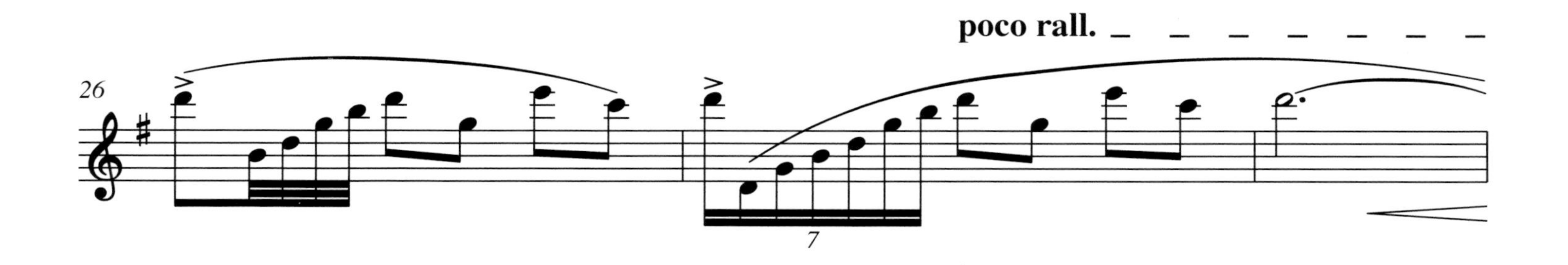

Grade 3

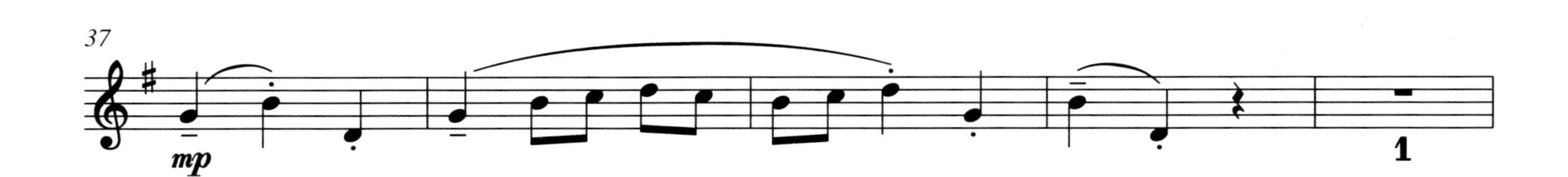

Cloud Nine

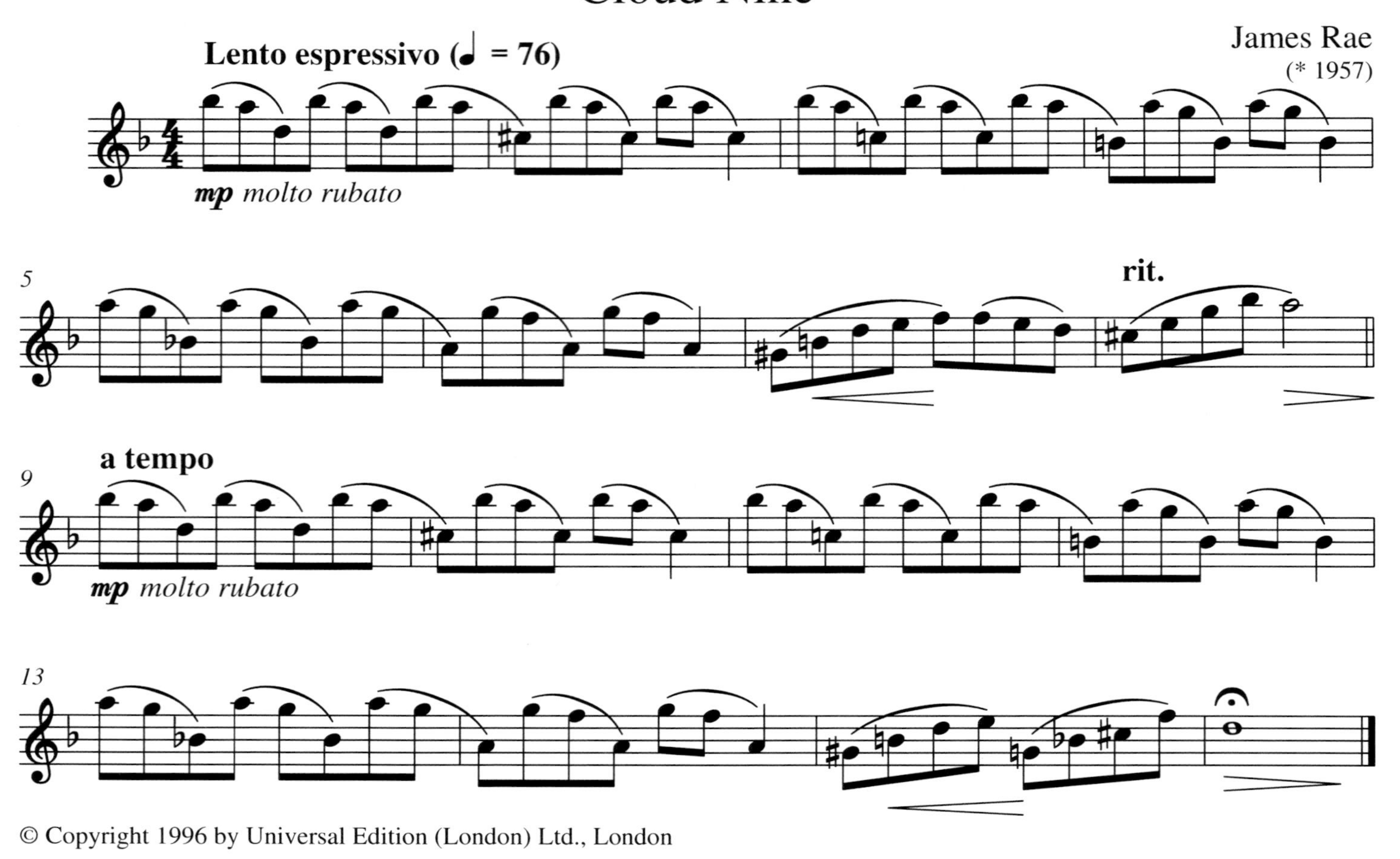

Grade 3

Flute Un-Plugged

Selected Titles in Jazz Styles for Flute

EASY

UE 21 320 Easy Blue Flute Duets (2 fl.) *James Rae*
UE 16 581 Easy Jazzy Flute (fl. & piano) *James Rae*
UE 16 587 Easy Jazzy Duets – Flutes (2 fl.) *James Rae*
UE 16 588 Easy Jazzy Duets – Flute and Clarinet (fl. & clar.) *James Rae*
UE 18 825 Jazzy Flute Vol 1 (fl. & piano) *James Rae*
UE 21 101 Play It Cool (fl. & piano or CD) *James Rae*

EASY TO INTERMEDIATE

UE 19 360 Jazzy Flute Vol 2 (fl. & piano) *James Rae*
UE 19 184 Christmas Jazz – Flute (fl. & piano) *James Rae*
UE 17 362 Latin Flute (fl. & piano) *James Rae*
UE 21 357 Jazz Zone – Flute (fl. & CD) *James Rae*

EASY TO ADVANCED

UE 19 184 40 Modern Studies (fl. solo) *James Rae*

INTERMEDIATE

UE 19 429 Jazzy Duets – Flutes (2 fl.) *James Rae*
UE 19 396 Jazzy Duets – Flute and Clarinet (fl. & clar.) *James Rae*
UE 19 763 Blue Flute (fl. & piano) *James Rae*
UE 19 710 Blue Flute & Saxophone Duets (fl. & alto sax.) *James Rae*

731/IV 06

Classical Repertoire for Flute

Easy

Camille Saint-Saëns, from 'The Carnival of the Animals' (2 fl. & pno) *arr. Barbara Dobretsberger*	UE 30 349
Peter Iljitsch Tschaikowsky, from 'The Nutcracker' (2 fl. & pno) *arr. Barbara Dobretsberger*	UE 30 357
Edvard Grieg, from 'Geer Gynt' (2 fl. & pno) *arr. Barbara Dobretsberger*	UE 30 350
James Rae, Play it Cool – Flute (fl. & pno, fl. & CD)	UE 21 101
James Rae, Easy Blue Flute Duets (2 fl.)	UE 21 320

Easy to Intermediate

125 Easy Classical Studies *Ed. Frans Vester*	UE 16 042
100 Classical Studies *Ed. Frans Vester*	UE 12 992
James Rae, Style Workout – Studies in classical, jazz, rock and latin styles	UE 21 319

Intermediate

50 Classical Studies *Ed. Frans Vester*	UE 14 672
Notebook for Anna Magdalena Bach (fl. & pno) *arr. Ulrich Müller-Doppler & Peter Ludwig*	UE 32 921
W. A. Mozart, from 'The Magic Flute' (2 fl.) *arr. Gerhard Braun*	UE 15 966
W. A. Mozart, from 'Don Giovanni' (2 fl.) *arr. Karl Heinz Füssl*	UE 17 284
W. A. Mozart, from 'Marriage of Figaro' (2 fl.) *arr. Gerhard Braun*	UE 16 773
W. A. Mozart, from 'Abduction from the Seraglio' (2 fl.) *arr. Gerhard Braun*	UE 16 737
Classic Duets for Flute (2 fl.) *Ed. Mary Karen Clardy*	
Vol. 1	UE 70 005
Vol. 2	UE 70 078
Magic Flute Ensemble 1 – The Renaissance (3–5 fl. & CD) *arr. Barbara Gisler-Haase*	UE 31 912
Magic Flute Ensemble 2 – The Romantic Era (3–5 fl. & CD) *arr. Barbara Gisler-Haase*	UE 32 652
Play-Along Flute from Bach to Satie (fl. & CD) *arr. Barbara Gisler-Haase*	UE 31 788
Erik Satie, 3 Gymnopédies (fl. & pno) *arr. Sylvia C. Rosin*	UE 32 988
Claude Debussy, 8 Selected Pieces (fl. & pno) *arr. P. Kolman*	UE 18 018
Claude Debussy, from 'Children's Corner' (2 fl. & pno) *arr. Joseph Diermaier*	UE 31 787
Nikolai Rimskij-Korsakow, from 'Sheherazade' (2 fl. & pno) *arr. Joseph Diermaier*	UE 31 205

Advanced

Frank Martin, Ballade (fl. & pno) *Ed. Paula Robison*	UE 70 049
Classic Flute Solos (fl.) with demonstr. CD *Ed. Mary Karen Clardy*	UE 70 079

729/V 06